A Reminder for Emily

An Electrical Engineering Story

Written by the Engineering is Elementary Team
Illustrated by Ross Sullivan-Wiley

Chapter One Visiting the Sheep

"Bessie! Come here, girl!" I called our biggest sheep over to the side of the pen. I did want to say hi to Bessie, but what I really wanted was for her new baby lamb, Molly, to follow her. Bessie trotted over and Molly came behind, wiggling a bit on her tiny, thin legs. I reached down to stroke Molly's soft wool.

"Look how beautiful you are," I said. Bessie bleated at me. "You too, Bessie. You look lovely as a new mum."

Actually, Bessie was more of an old mum than a new mum. We'd brought Bessie to our station—the ranch we live on—almost six years ago, when I was just a little girl. In that time she'd had lots of lambs, but Molly was one of my favorites.

I glanced in their drinking trough and saw that there was only a bit of water left in the bottom. I sighed.

"I guess I should go out to the well and bring over a few buckets of water," I said. I loved all our sheep, especially Bessie and Molly, but hauling water to their trough was one of my least favorite chores. The crank on our well stuck, the water was heavy, and somehow I always managed to soak myself with the waves that sloshed out of the top of the bucket. I looked towards the trough again.

"Maybe I can wait a little longer . . . " I looked at Bessie and Molly. "I'm just going to go out riding for a bit. Then I'll come right back to fill up the trough. Wish me luck on my jumps!" With another bleat from Bessie, I jogged off to our horse stables.

Chapter Two | The Big Jump

I crouched down and braced my legs against the saddle as my horse, Flash, tensed before leaping over a jump. My curly hair bounced over my shoulders and my stomach dropped as Flash and I hung for a moment in midair. Flash hit the ground running. I pulled on the anchors, reining Flash in, and we fell into a slow trot.

"Yes!" I cried, pumping my fist in the air. I pulled the anchors and turned Flash around. The new jumping fence that I'd built was made out of beams from an old tool shed Dad had taken down. It had to be at least a meter high—a new record for us!

Dad will be so proud! I thought. I'd been riding horses with my dad on the rocky trails around our station pretty much since I could crawl. Mum wouldn't let me start jumping until I was older, and now I'm finally starting to practice high jumps. When he was younger, my dad competed in show jumping competitions. He told me that in a year or so, if I kept practicing really hard, I'd probably be good enough to compete myself! Now Dad was gone for a few weeks to a meeting for Australian station owners. I really wanted to master this jump before he came back.

I trotted Flash up a hill overlooking our station and stared at the outback around me. "It feels like we're out in the wilderness, huh, Flash?" I asked. The spot where I

practice jumps with Flash is less than half a kilometer away from our house, but looking at the rusty orange land in front of me made me feel like I was worlds away. In the distance two kangaroos hopped toward a watering hole.

"Good thing Dad's not here," I said. Dad hates the way the kangaroos always get into things on the station and make a mess. But I think it's fun to watch the kangaroos jumping around. As they hopped out of sight, I watched the bright red sun slipping towards the horizon.

"I love the sunset," I said. "Wait . . . sunset? What time is it?" I turned Flash around and looked at the sheep's shed.

"Oh no, oh no . . ." I grumbled. I squeezed Flash's sides and galloped back towards the shed.

Chapter Three No More Practice

I hopped off Flash and wrapped his anchors around a post. I jogged over to the well and filled a bucket. Water sloshed all over my arms as I lifted the bucket up and carried it to the door of the shed.

Darn! Mum was already there, holding my new baby brother, Andrew, and petting Bessie. I didn't need to look at the trough to know that I'd been late to get Bessie's water and Mum had come to do it for me. Slowly I let the bucket slide down to the floor.

"Emily," Mum began. "Are you all right?" Mum's eyebrow was raised into a pointy arch. I knew that look—I was in big trouble.

"I'm fine," I said. "I just lost track of time."

Mum sighed. “Emily, that’s not a good excuse. You can’t leave the sheep without water,” she said, pointing to their trough. “Everyone on this station has chores to do. When your dad’s away, he and I need extra help from you, especially now that I’m also taking care of Andrew. Your irresponsibility has got to stop.”

Irresponsible. That's a word that I'd come to know well. I love riding Flash so much that sometimes I push everything else aside. I could feel my cheeks get redder than they already were. I looked down towards the ground.

"I'm sorry," I said. "I just get wrapped up in my jumping. I can't believe I let Bessie and Molly down."

"I know it's easy to get caught up in your riding and jumping," Mum said, "but these chores are important. It's okay for you to go out riding in the afternoon, but you have to make sure you're back before the sheep are out of water." I felt tears welling up in my eyes and heard Mum sigh. "You know how much Andrew depends on me. Bessie and her new baby lamb depend on you to keep them strong and healthy in the same way. Until you can show me that you're responsible enough to take your chores seriously and bring water to the sheep every day, no more riding Flash."

I wanted to argue, but I knew Mum was right. I couldn't believe that my stupid mistake was going to cost me my afternoons of horseback riding. Right when Flash and I were getting really good at our new jump!

Mum touched my shoulder and changed the subject.

"Come on," Mum said. "Bring Flash back to the stables and wipe him down. We should get you out of those dirty riding clothes before dinner. We're going over to Pete and Sarah's house."

"Pete and Sarah's!" I said, starting to smile. At least it wouldn't be an entirely bad day. I always had fun at Pete and Sarah's house.

Chapter Four | A Trip to Pete and Sarah's

Pete and Sarah were our closest neighbors, even though they lived over a kilometer away. They had just moved to the outback a few months ago after Pete retired. He used to work for a company in Sydney—Australia's biggest city. I'd seen pictures of Sydney's famous opera house and I thought it looked like a neat place to visit. *I wonder what it would be like to take Flash through those streets. Maybe we could jump over some city park benches.*

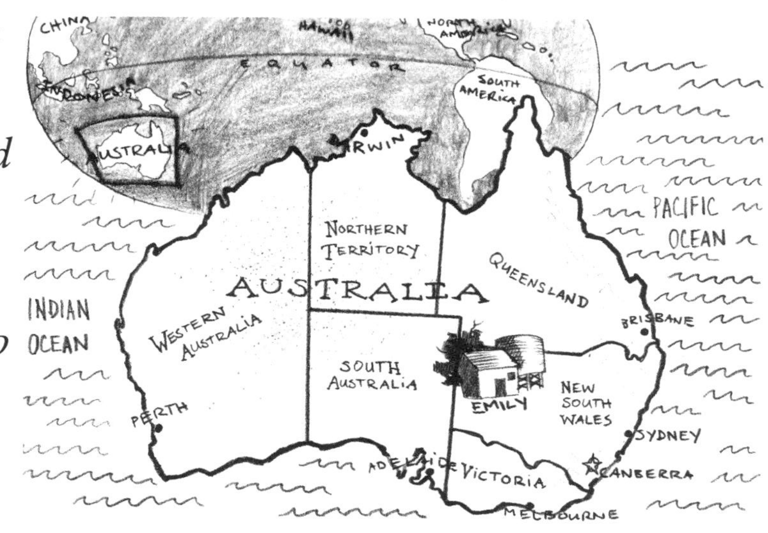

Mum and I each held a flashlight to guide us through the evening darkness. I pushed Andrew's stroller up the gravel drive leading to Pete and Sarah's house. When we got close, Mum knew what I was thinking even before I asked her. "You go ahead. I'll bring up Andrew's stroller." I grinned and ran up to the kitchen door, jerked it open, and came up behind Sarah to give her a big hug.

"Goodness, who is that behind me?" she said. "You almost made me drop the breadbasket." Sarah turned and kissed me on the cheek. "How beautiful you look! And that hair. I would've loved red hair like that when I was young." I did a little twirl for her. I knew Sarah was going to comment on my outfit. I'd put on one of my best dresses to come to dinner and tied my hair back in a bow. Sarah was wearing a dress too, as usual, and her Australian opal necklace sparkled under the kitchen lights.

"You look like a proper little lady," Sarah said. "If only you looked this way all the time, and didn't wear the ragtag clothing you call your riding gear."

"Jeans and a T-shirt are the most comfortable clothes for jumping," I said. "And I do like to wear fancy dresses sometimes. Maybe I'd wear them all the time if I could do jumps in them!"

Sarah chuckled as she bustled over to the door. "Let me

go help your mother with the stroller," Sarah said, just as Pete came in the kitchen.

"G'day, Miss Emily!" he bellowed. "What have you got to show me today?"

I hugged Pete around his waist and began pointing out all my new scrapes and bruises. "I got this one from skidding against some bark when I steered Flash too close to a tree," I said, sticking my elbow up towards him. "And this one from a rock out by the lake," I said, pointing to my knee.

"And what about that one?" Pete asked, pointing to my bruised thumb.

"Oh," I said, feeling my cheeks get hot and pink. "That's from when I was using a hammer and nails to build my new jump. I missed the nail."

"Onya," Pete said, laughing. "Great job. Those are some serious battle scars. Who would ever guess this little lady would be working on such fierce horse jumps?"

"Yup, I landed a big jump perfectly today!"

"That's my girl," Pete said.

"But I'm in trouble, Pete," I said, lowering my voice. "I stayed out with Flash too late today and I forgot to fill the sheep's trough. Mum isn't going to let me out to practice in the afternoons anymore." Before I could say more, Mum and Andrew came in and Sarah hustled us all to sit down at the table.

Chapter Five An Alarming Experience

After dinner Sarah shooed Pete and me out of the kitchen so she and Mum could chat and have tea. I didn't mind. That meant Pete and I could head out to his shed. That's where Pete keeps all his gadgets. Sometimes when he's working in the shed, he'll let me take apart one of the old radios he has or make sculptures out of coils of metal wire lying around.

"What are you working on now, Pete?" I asked.

Pete patted the rusty green frame of a lawn mower. "Well, this old lawn mower is clapped out. I've got to fix up the engine so I can cut the grass over by Sarah's garden."

I hopped on a stool next to Pete and told him all about the new jump I'd just practiced. I could tell he was listening even as he hammered, unscrewed, and cleaned different parts of the lawn mower.

"And then we rode up to the jump," I said, "so fast that I thought Flash was going to run right into it instead of over it, and—" *Beep! Beep! Beep! Beep!*

Pete laughed as I whipped around towards the noise and almost fell off my stool. When I turned, I noticed the light above the shed door was flashing. "What's going on?" I asked.

"That's one of my newest technologies," Pete said. "Sarah was complaining that when she would yell out to the shed to tell me that lunch was ready, I wouldn't hear her. Sometimes I'd be running one of my tools that makes a lot of noise, and, well, my old ears aren't exactly what they used to be. Sometimes I just plain didn't hear her calling. I realized I needed some thing or process—a technology—to help me solve the problem. So I rigged up a buzzer system. When Sarah wants me to come in, she can press a button I wired up in the kitchen. Then the buzzer sounds and the light flashes in the shed. I can see the light blinking even if I'm using a loud tool and I don't hear the buzzer. It keeps me out of trouble with Sarah," he said with a wink.

"Maybe I need one, too. I wish I had something to keep me out of trouble," I said. *Hmm*, I thought. *An alarm to keep me out of trouble. What an idea.* "Hey, Pete, what if I had an alarm to tell me when the sheep's water trough is low? You can see the shed from almost everywhere around the horse stables—I'd definitely see a flashing light. And if I were close enough I'd hear the buzzer. Could you help me make an alarm?"

"You're always one to present a challenge, Emily," Pete said. "I think we could work on one together. The tricky part will be figuring out a way to make sure the alarm is safe. Water conducts electricity. That means electricity can pass through it and give you a shock, or worse. Have you ever noticed a warning label on some electronics that shows a triangle with a jagged arrow through it? That's to warn you about the danger of electrocution if you use them near the water," he said.

I nodded. "So this is a bad idea," I said.

"No, no," Pete said. "We'll just have to be extra careful. The fact that water conducts electricity is just one piece of the puzzle. Some materials are conductors, and others aren't. We can use that knowledge to help us. If we use a material that isn't a conductor to keep the water and the electricity separate, that will prevent anyone from getting hurt. Don't worry, we'll work it out. In the meantime, maybe you can find some materials to help us get started."

"Where should I look?" I asked.

"If you just take apart some of the junk I have around

here, you'll find lots of things you could use," Pete said. "Old radios and other electronics have lots of wires and switches inside."

"Pete," I asked, "how do you know how to make all these things?"

"I used to create all sort of neat things like that for my job before I retired," Pete said. "I was an electrical engineer. That's someone who uses what they know about science, math, and their creativity to solve problems involving electricity. I worked on all sorts of interesting projects, like helping to create hearing aids for tiny babies, and working on devices that helped to track whales by the sounds they make."

"Pete, that's great!" I cried.

Pete chuckled. "It was a lot of fun. But that's enough about me. Sarah and your mum are probably wondering where we are. Come on."

Chapter Six | Convincing Mum

As I walked home next to Mum and Andrew's stroller, I told Mum about my plan to build an alarm to let me know when the sheep needed water. "This way, when I'm riding Flash and practicing my jumps, I'll have a system to let me know when I should come back." I glanced up at her, trying to guess what she was thinking. "What do you say?"

Mum walked in silence for a few moments. "I think this sounds like a good idea, Emily," said Mum. "I'm glad you're taking this problem seriously and trying to come up with a solution. If you can get an alarm working and show me that it will help you do your chores on time, you can start jumping before dinner again." Mum paused for a moment and smiled. "With all the handiwork you do to build jumps for Flash, I have no doubt you'll be able to build an alarm system."

I was so excited that Mum liked my alarm idea. I couldn't wait to see Pete again so we could get started.

Chapter Seven: Engineering with Electricity

"All right, Pete," I said, rushing into his shed. "I'm ready to tear open a radio and get this alarm set up!"

"Easy there, jillaroo," Pete said. "Before we start tearing things apart, I think we need to come up with a plan. And get some biscuits. Here, Sarah made a batch just for your visit."

I took a bite of biscuit and chewed for a few moments. "Why do we need a plan?" I asked. "Can't we just figure things out as we go along?"

"Sometimes you can," Pete said. "But when I was working as an engineer, there were steps that we would follow whenever we were trying to solve a problem. We call the steps the engineering design process. And since you're about to work on your very first electrical engineering problem, it might be a good idea for us to try using the process. Come take a seat over here and give me a better idea of what we're trying to design."

I sat down next to Pete by his workbench.

"The first step of the engineering design process is asking some good questions," said Pete. "Do you want this alarm to go off at a certain time of day, or just when the sheep's water trough is getting low?"

"Hmm," I said. "I guess I just want it to let me know when the water is low. If I'm out riding and I'm practicing a new jump, I don't want to have to stop just because it's a certain time. I'd rather wait till I really need to go to the shed."

"Sounds good to me," said Pete. "Do you know where you want the light and the buzzer to go?"

I pictured the way the shed looked from the stables. "Um, maybe the light could go on the top of the shed, and the buzzer could go on the back of the shed, facing away from the house. That way it won't be too loud for the sheep—or for Andrew."

We went on like that for almost the whole morning. Pete had me imagine a few different setups, or designs, for the alarm system. Then he had me draw a plan.

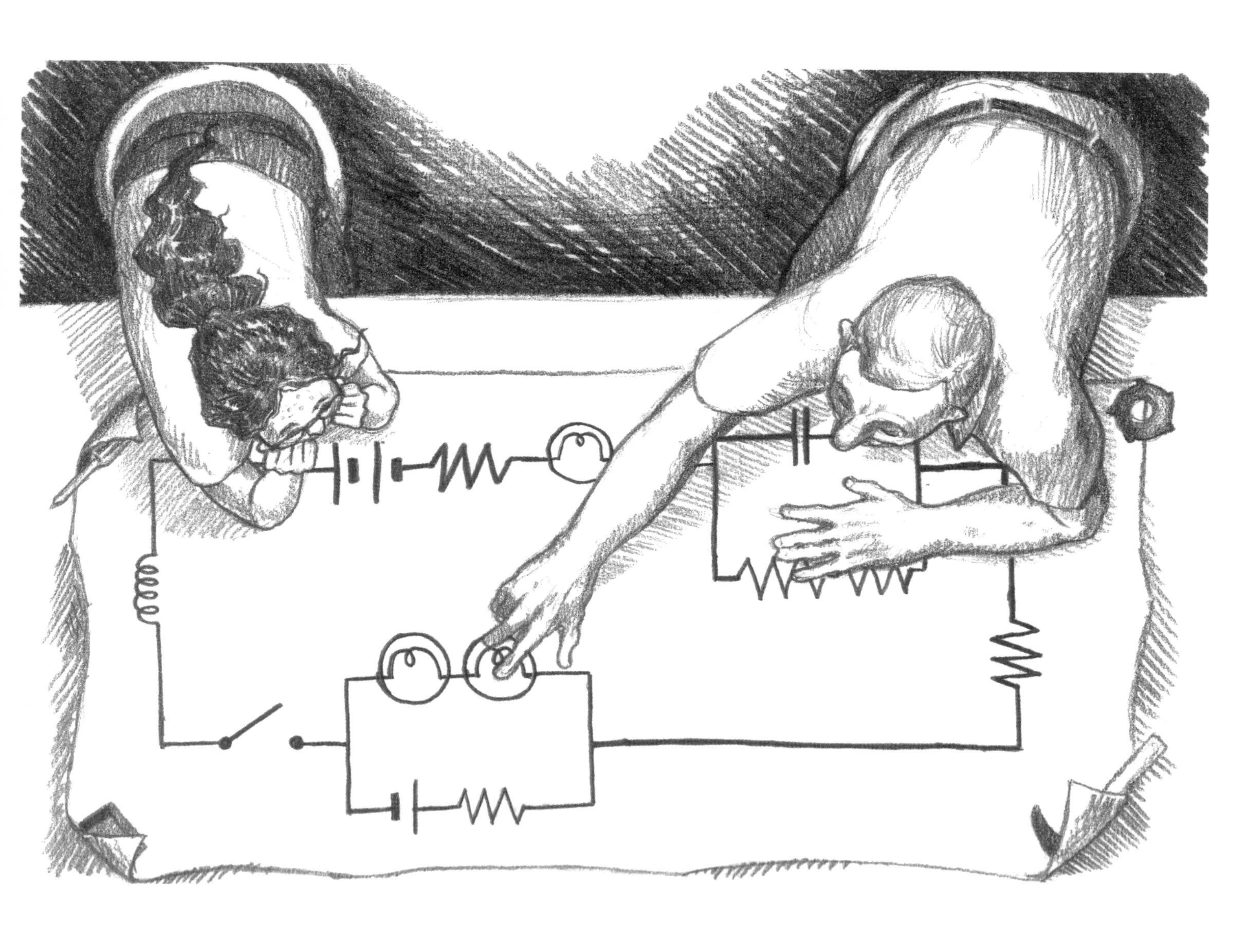

“Let me show you the plan that I did for my alarm system,” Pete said. “Electrical engineers call plans like these schematic diagrams.” He rummaged through a cabinet next to his workbench and pulled out a piece of paper with some lines and pictures on it.

“How could this be your plan—I mean schematic

diagram?" I asked. "I don't see the light or the buzzer on it."

"Ahh, but they are here. I just used symbols," Pete explained. "You see, electrical engineers and other people who work with electricity know that the symbol for a light looks like a circle with a swirl through it. The wires that connect everything are the lines in between the pictures. And the space here that looks like a door swinging open, that's the switch that closes the loop and makes the light and buzzer go off. It completes the system—or what we call the circuit. Using these symbols is kind of like speaking a language. The symbols allow us to communicate easily with one another."

"So altogether, everything that you've drawn here symbolizes a circuit?" I asked.

"Exactly!" Pete said. "Now why don't you try making a schematic diagram of your own. Then, once we have that all set, we can move on to the next step of the engineering design process: creating!"

Chapter Eight | Completing the Circuit

The next day, after I had a schematic diagram drawn up, Pete helped me put together a miniature model to test my circuit. After everything was wired, he gave me a thumbs-up sign, letting me know it was okay to flip the switch to test the alarm. *Beep! Beep! Beep!* The buzzer was working! But the light wasn't.

"Pete!" I said. "What's wrong?"

"It looks like we may need to fix this wiring," he said.

"What do you mean?" I asked. "I connected the wire to the light bulb. What else matters?"

"Well, electricity isn't something magical that will light up a bulb just because it's nearby," Pete explained. "To wire the circuit correctly, you need to make it so the electric current

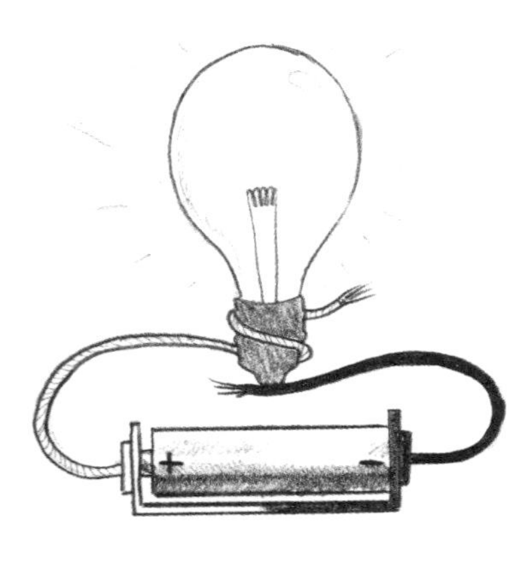

can flow into the bulb at one point, and out of the bulb at another point. There have to be two points of contact to complete the circuit. I'll show you."

Pete took the one wire that I had wrapped around the light bulb and connected it to just one side of the bulb's base. Then he used another wire to connect the bottom of the bulb to the battery.

"Ta da!" he said. "Let there be light."

"I see how that works," I said. "So is that how all the lights in our house work, too?"

"Yes, it's very similar," he said. "Except in this setup, we're using some batteries to get our electricity. The electricity in your house is powered by the generator you have in your backyard and the solar panels on top of your house. People who live in cities get electricity from a power generation plant. It travels from the plant through wires right into their houses. No matter how different the sources might look, they all generate electrical energy."

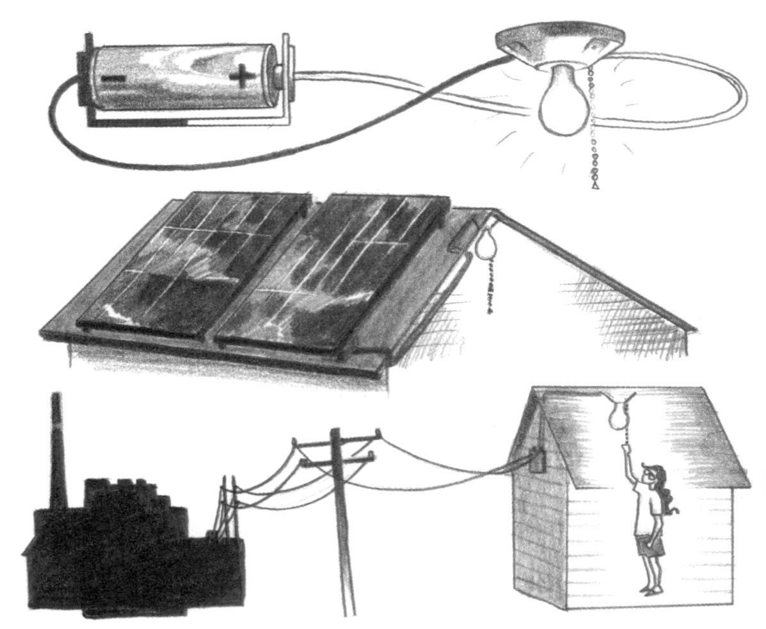

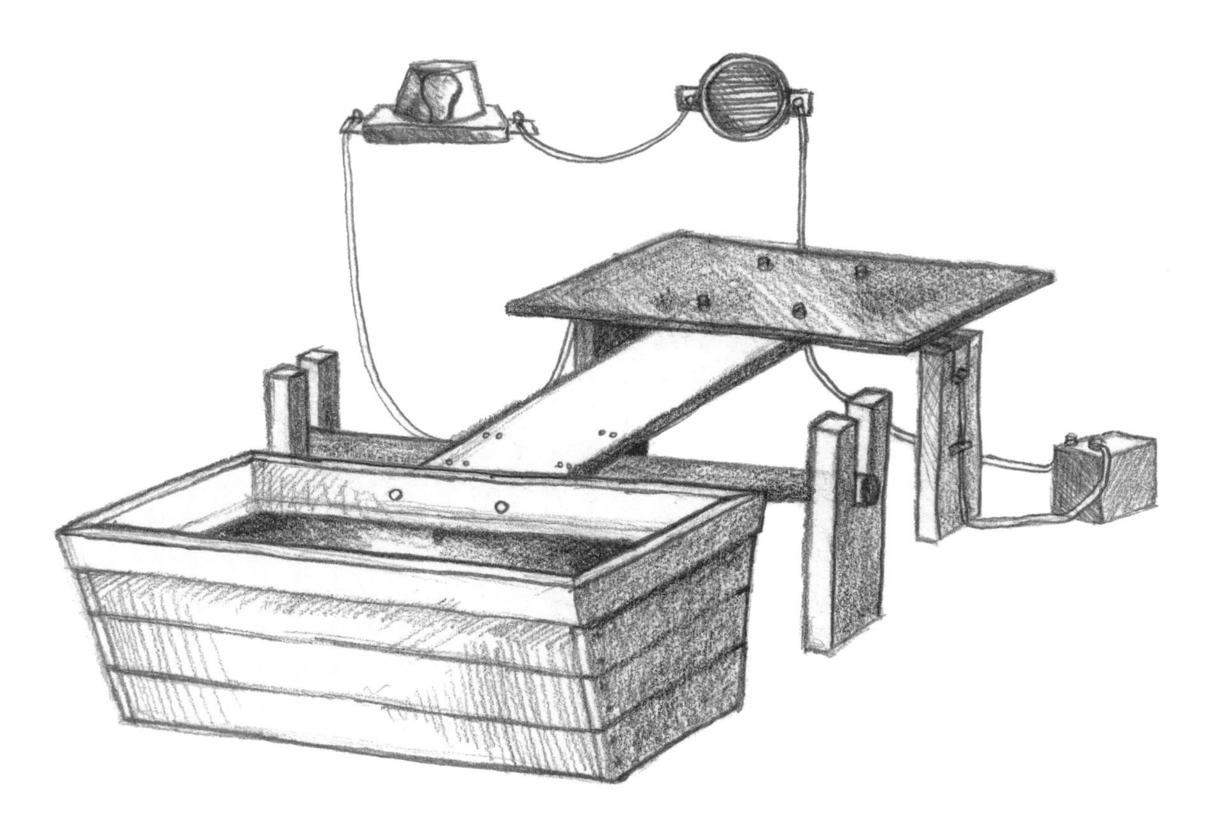

"That's pretty cool," I said. "I didn't realize there were so many different ways to generate electricity."

Pete and I worked for the whole weekend to put my alarm system together. We even came up with a nifty switch made out of a big wooden lever. Since wood doesn't conduct electricity, the circuit was safe for me and for the sheep. One end of the lever held the trough, and we attached a piece of metal to the other end. When the trough was full, the weight of the water held the switch open. But when the water level was low, the lever would swing down to complete the circuit. Then the light would flash and the buzzer would buzz! I couldn't wait to show my alarm to everyone.

Chapter Nine | By Jingoes!

Monday morning I heard voices in the kitchen when I woke up. Dad!

I flew out of bed and into the kitchen. "Em!" Dad said. "Did you miss me?" Holding Andrew in one arm, he wrapped the other around me, giving me a hug and a kiss.

"Of course! But I designed something really special while you were gone that I want you and Mum to come see!" I led Mum and Dad out to the shed.

"Now pretend the sheep have drunk almost all of their water. The trough will get lighter and it will close this switch." I began scooping water out of the trough with a bucket to demonstrate. *Beep! Beep! Beep!* We heard the buzzer on the outside of the barn ringing. "And there's a light on top of the barn that flashes, too!"

Dad's mouth dropped open and Mum smiled broadly. Even Bessie and Molly seemed interested, poking their muzzles around the new trough.

"By jingoes, Em," Dad said. "Mum told me you had a solution to make sure you're on time to do your chores, but I never imagined anything like this. How did you ever put this together?"

"Pete helped me," I said. "He taught me all about electricity and designing things."

"You really did think of everything," said Mum. "But I guess I shouldn't be too surprised. When it comes to jumping and riding, you're very persistent."

"I do love jumping with Flash," I said, "but really I did this for Molly. Oof—" I felt a push from behind and turned to see Bessie prodding me with her nose. "Okay, and for you too, Bessie!" I said, giggling.

Try It!

Design an Alarm Circuit

Try making an alarm just like the one Emily and Pete made! Your goal will be to build a switch, find a conductor, and then design an alarm circuit.

Materials

- ☐ Alligator clips
- ☐ Tape
- ☐ Cardboard
- ☐ D-cell battery
- ☐ Film canister
- ☐ Battery holder
- ☐ Popcorn kernels
- ☐ Rock or large marble
- ☐ Small paper cup
- ☐ Metal tack or glue
- ☐ Holiday light or bulb and bulb holder
- ☐ Possible conductors, such as paper clips, aluminum foil, coins, thimbles, etc.

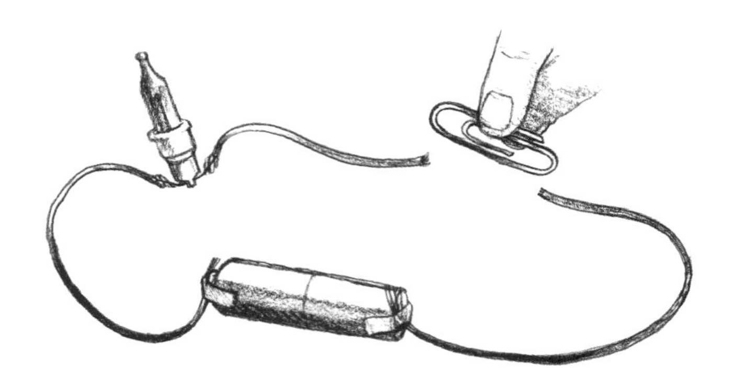

Build a Switch

Build a switch similar to the switch Emily and Pete designed. Ask an adult to help you cut a 9" by 2.5" piece of cardboard. Tape the cardboard on top of a film canister so that the cardboard moves like a seesaw. Tape a small paper cup to one end of the cardboard. That will be your trough. Tape a rock or marble to the other end as a counterweight. DO NOT use water in your sheep trough! (Do you remember why Pete said that could be dangerous?) Use popcorn kernels or small beads instead.

Test Various Conductors

Create a circuit (as in the diagram above) in which you can test the possible conductors. Connect one stripped end of wire from your bulb to the battery. Using another piece of wire or an alligator clip, connect that wire to the other end of the battery. If you don't have a battery holder, just tape the wires in place. Use each of the possible conductors, one at a time, to complete the circuit. Do all of the materials make the light shine? Do some materials make the light shine brighter than others?

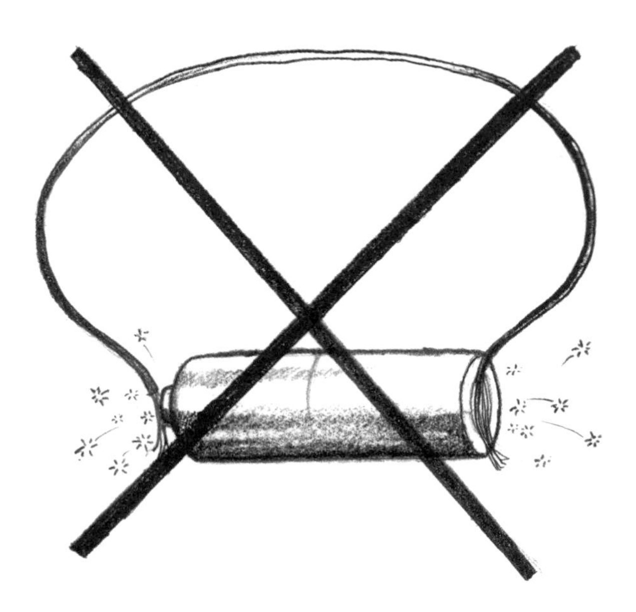

Warning: Do not connect the battery end-to-end with a wire. This will create a short circuit and can cause a fire.

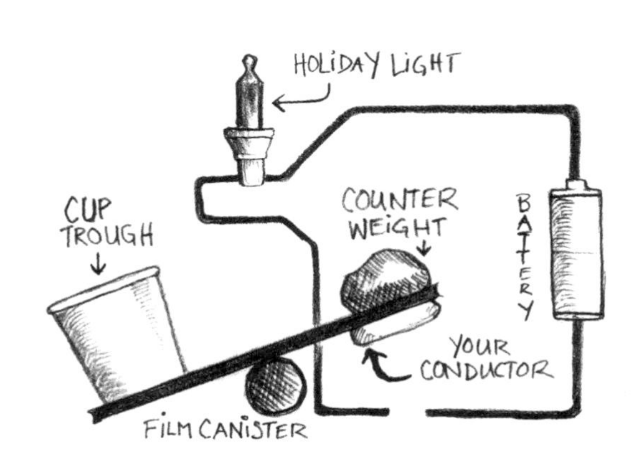

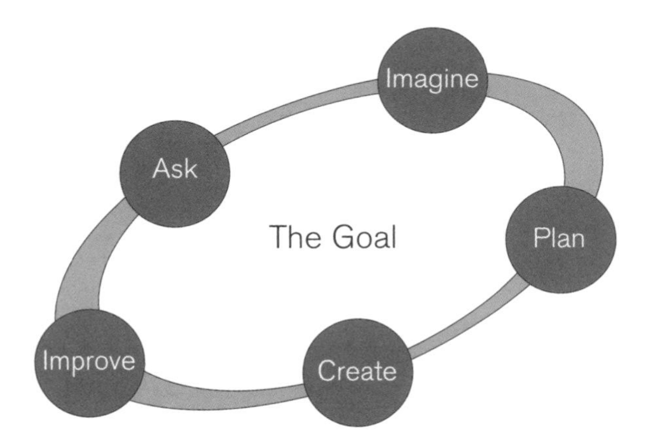

Design an Alarm Circuit

Now that you've experimented with materials to find a good conductor, can you design an alarm circuit using your switch? Place the conductor that you've chosen on the cardboard underneath the counterweight. You want your switch to turn the light on when the trough is empty. Where should you place it in the circuit to make the light shine? Are you able to turn the light on and off? How many kernels of corn do the sheep need to eat before the alarm goes off?

Improve Your Alarm Circuit

Use the engineering design process to improve your circuit design. Research different conductors. Could you put two lights in your circuit?

See What Others Have Done

See what other kids have done at http://www.mos.org/eie/tryit. What did you try? You can submit your solutions and pictures to our website, and maybe we'll post your submission!

Glossary

Anchors: Australian slang for reins of a horse.

Battery: One or more units that produce electrical energy.

Biscuit: Australian word for cookie.

By Jingoes: Australian phrase expressing surprise.

Circuit: The complete path of an electric current, including the source of electrical energy.

Clapped Out: Australian phrase meaning "broken down, won't work."

Conductor: A substance or body that allows electricity to pass through it.

Electrical Engineer: A person who works in the field of engineering concerned with solving problems involving electricity.

Electricity: A form of energy that is found in nature (lightning), but that can also be artificially produced by people (with a generator).

Engineer: A person who uses his or her creativity and understanding of mathematics and science to design things that solve problems.

Engineering Design Process: The steps that engineers use to design something to solve a problem.

Generator: A machine that converts mechanical energy into electrical energy.

Jillaroo: Australian word for a female station (or ranch) worker.

Kilometer: A unit of measurement equal to about 0.62 miles.

Onya: Australian phrase of congratulations meaning "good on you."

Schematic Diagram: An illustration of an electrical circuit with the components represented by their symbols.

Station: Australian word for ranch.

Technology: Any thing or process that people create and use to solve a problem.